I LOVE MYTHOLOGY

The Trojan War

Texts: Anastasia D. Makri

Illustration: Nickos Maroulakis

Translated from Greek into English

Kiriaki Papakonstantinou

BA English Language & Literature / MA Psycholinguistics / DIPTRANS - DPSI
Chartered Linguist (Translator) / Translators - Interpreters Trainer
Member of the Chartered Institute of Linguists in London

UNDER THE AEGIS OF

UNESCO
United Nations
Educational, Scientific
& Cultural Organization

ΟΜΙΛΟΣ ΓΙΑ ΤΗΝ UNESCO ΝΟΜΟΥ ΠΕΙΡΑΙΩΣ & ΝΗΣΩΝ
CLUB FOR UNESCO OF THE DEPARTMENT OF PIRAEUS & ISLANDS
Πέτρου Ράλλη 210 & Θησέως 1 Νίκαια,
Τηλ.: 210 4967757, Fax: 210 4944564 - www.unescopireas.gr e-mail: unescop@otenet.gr

AGYRA
publications

The Apple of Discord

In Phthia a big feast was held. King Peleus was getting married to the eldest daughter of Nereus, Thetis. The matchmaker of this wedding, which was held in Olympus, was Zeus himself. All gods were invited except Eris, the goddess of discord. So, when she heard it she was furious with anger. To avenge them, she took a golden apple and wrote on it: "To the Fairest".

That is: The most beautiful goddess should get it.

Then she rolled the apple in front of Hera, Athena and Aphrodite. Each one claimed the apple for herself and eventually began to quarrel bitterly over the apple. Then Zeus, and the other gods, got in a rather difficult position. No matter which goddess they favoured, they would earn the enmity of the other two. For this reason, Zeus decided to end the quarrel and send them to an arbitrator. He called Hermes and told him to lead the three goddesses to Mount Ida, in Troy. There, Paris, the son of King Priam of Troy, would decide which the prettiest one was.

Hermes immediately executed the command of Zeus and instantly, the three goddesses were found in front of a handsome shepherd, Paris. How come a prince had become a shepherd? Here's the explanation!

3

When the queen Hecabe, Priam's wife, gave birth to Paris, her youngest son, the king had a terrible nightmare: that this child would bring about the destruction of Troy. To prevent such harm, Priam sent him off to the mountain, where he was raised by a bear. When he grew up, he became a shepherd.

Aphrodite wins the Apple of Discord

When Paris saw the goddesses and the wing-foot god, Hermes, remained speechless. Then Hermes approached him and explained what he had to do. The three goddesses, astonished by Paris' beauty, each tried to win him over, so they resorted to bribes. Hera promised him that if she was offered that Apple she would make him ruler of the whole world. Athena promised to make him wise, and, finally, Aphrodite promised him the love of the most beautiful woman in the world, Helen, Queen of Sparta. Paris thought for a moment and then, kneeling before Aphrodite, offered her the golden apple.

The Abduction of Helen

It was not long before Paris was the winner of an archery competition held in Ilion. When Priam was about to laurel him, he asked the young man what his lineage was.

Then Paris told him the story of his life, and that he was raised by a bear. Priam was touched as he realized that the young man standing in front of him was his son and decided to welcome him in his family. Paris, all excited about his new life, threw himself to the pleasures and luxuries of the palace. Eventually, he told his father that he wanted to travel and visit new places. Of course, he did not reveal his real purpose to seize Helen of Sparta.

The journey was not easy. However, with the help of Aphrodite, Paris managed to get to Sparta. There, he was welcomed by King Menelaus. But, when the king had to leave Sparta for a while, Paris found the opportunity, seized Helen with the treasures of the palace and returned to Troy.

When Menelaus heard what had happened, was outraged and asked all other kings of Greece to help him. So, together they decided to make war in order to pay off this assault. They gathered at the harbour of Aulis to sail off. The only king absent was Achilles, whose mother, Thetis, had hidden him in the palace of the king of Skyros. However, ingenious Ulysses discovered him and persuaded him to follow them.

The Sacrifice of Iphigenia

Menelaus' brother, Agamemnon, King of Mycenae, was the leader of the Greek army in this campaign. They were ready to sail off, but the favorable wind ceased. The seer Calchas said that goddess Artemis was punishing Agamemnon for killing one of her sacred deer, and kept the winds. The only way to appease her anger was Agamemnon to sacrifice his first-born daughter, Iphigenia.

Agamemnon with a heavy heart asked his wife Clytemnestra to bring their daughter to Aulis, supposedly to marry her to dashing Achilles. The poor mother, unsuspecting, accompanied her daughter in her wedding-dress but on arriving at Aulis, instead of a wedding ceremony, sacrifice was the plan. Fortunately, the last minute Artemis changed her mind and grabbed the beautiful girl away from of the priest's hands, in a cloud. A deer took her place and this way Iphigenia was saved. Clytemnestra, however, vowed to avenge her husband.

The Greeks arrive at Troy

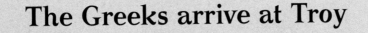

The Greeks sailed off, as soon as the trade wind started blowing and drawing of the sail. On arriving at Troy, they surrounded and besieged it.

However, nine years later, they had failed to enter the city. Several warriors were killed from both camps. Achilles and Priam's brave son, Hector, were among them. As far as the gods are concerned, some took side with the Greeks and others with the Trojans.

The Trojan Horse

For ten long years, the Greeks could not get over the wall of Troy in order the war to end. They were so tired, that they wanted to go back home. They were all desperate. Then, resourceful Ulysses suggested Agamemnon to build a huge wooden horse, hollow inside – the Trojan Horse. And so they did. Once they built the horse, they dragged and left it near the castle. Then they started spreading word about sailing away and leaving the horse as a gift offer to Apollo. Inside the horse, however, several men – including Ulysses – were hidden. The Trojans saw the wooden horse and dragged it into Ilion, dedicating it to their patron god, Apollo. King Priam's daughter, the seeress Cassandra and Apollo's priest, Laokoon, were crying out in vain that this was one of the

Greeks' trick and should not be fooled.

The Trojans thought they got rid of the Greeks. More than happy, they celebrated the end of the war with food and drink all day long. So, when night fell, they were all drunk and exhausted. No one expected what would follow...

11

The Destruction of Troy

That night, while the Trojan people slept soundly, the Greeks hidden inside the wooden horse climbed out and opened the gates of Troy. The Greek army rushed into the city and carnage started. Troy was wrapped in flames and the Greeks merciless killed everyone in their way, overnight. They looted the treasures they found in the palace and the rich houses. They destroyed even the temples. Eventually, they took Helen with them and burned the city to the ground.

No man of the royal family was left alive. The royal women – Hecuba, Cassandra and Andromache – were taken slaves, desperate for the loss of their family and the destruction of their land.

Returning Home

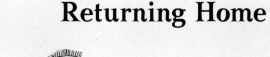

The journey home started. The gods, however, were very angry with the Greeks for destroying Troy. So, they decided to punish severely the resourceful Ulysses, who had the idea of the Trojan Horse and Agamemnon as well, who left the Greeks to put an entire city in mourning. So, when they were ready to sail off, the gods sowed discord between Menelaus, Agamemnon and Ulysses, and each one left separately.

The end of Agamemnon and the return of Menelaus

When Agamemnon decided to sacrifice his own daughter, Iphigenia, Clytemnestra's heart was filled with hatred for him. The years passed by and Clytemnestra did not expect her husband to return. Actually, she had married a young man, Aegisthus. She had her daughter, Electra, married to a poor villager so that her children would not have any right to the throne and had sent away her son, Orestes.

When Agamemnon arrived at the palace, he had with him Cassandra as slave. Clytemnestra pretended to be happy from his return. Cassandra, however, sensed the end of both herself and the king. And indeed, when Agamemnon finished his bath and Cassandra smeared him with perfume, Clytemnestra threw a veil on them and killed

14

them both. However, neither she nor Aegisthus had a better end. They were killed by her two children, who after that left Mycenae forever. This way, the kingdom of Agamemnon was eliminated.

As for Menelaus, he forgave Helen and took her home, where he arrived after many adventures. The gods punished him too and for seven years and struggled with the rough sea. When they arrived at Sparta, he lived the rest of his life peacefully.

15

What was left after the war ...

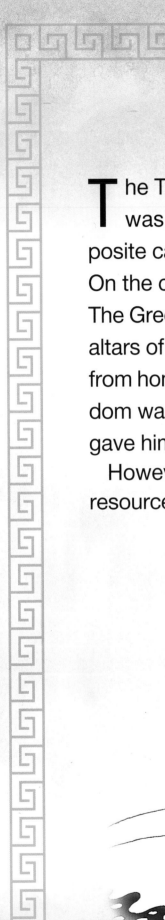

The Trojan War lasted for ten years. What was left of it was a miserable city, many people dead in both opposite camps, bitterness and pain. No war is of any good. On the contrary, it makes people show their worst selves. The Greeks showed respect to neither the temples nor the altars of the gods. Many of them left their last breath away from home. Agamemnon had a horrible death and his kingdom was extinguished. The treasures he brought with him gave him no happiness, nor saved his life.

However, the one who had the most difficult return was resourceful Ulysses...

By: Akis Melachris

Which path should King Menelaus follow
to get to his wife, Helen?

Color the dot pieces to see
what the hidden picture is.

18

Spot-the-Difference: Can you find the 9 differences between the picture and its negative?

Connect the dots from 1 to 35
to see what is sketched.

You can find out which is
the shadow of Paris?

21

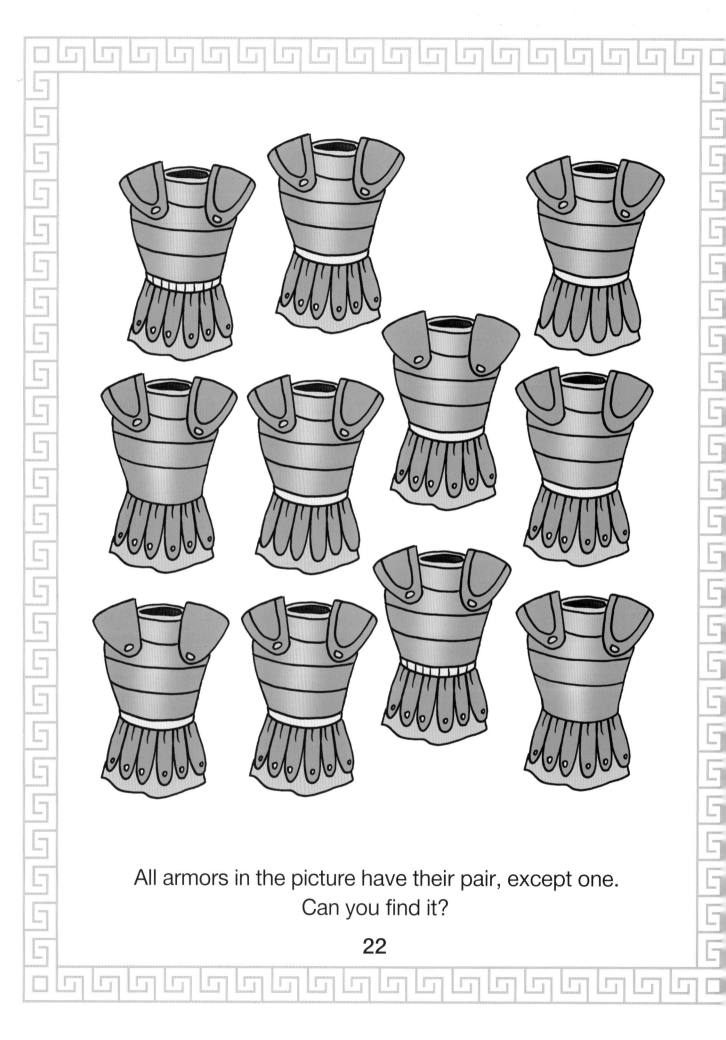

All armors in the picture have their pair, except one.
Can you find it?

22

1.   2.   3.

4.   5.   6.

Two out of the six details do not match the picture above.
Can you find which ones?

Put the letters in the correct order,
to see what Agamemnon wishes for.

In the picture there are two objects irrelevant
to the rest ones. Can you find them?

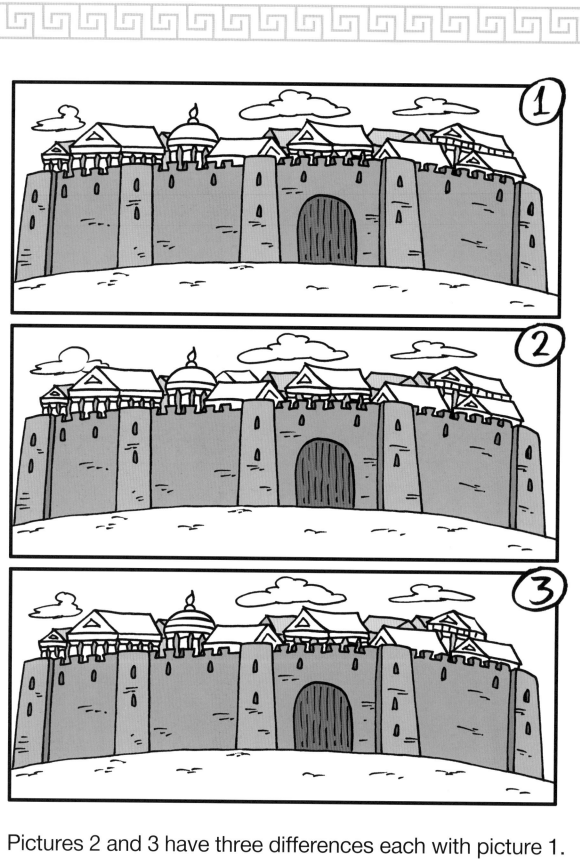

Pictures 2 and 3 have three differences each with picture 1.
Can you spot them?

26

Can you find out which is the shadow of Achilles?

C	A	S	S	I	U	F	R	I	C	H	E	H	O
O	F	M	A	W	T	U	H	E	C	A	B	E	S
R	R	E	X	A	Z	Q	U	A	R	B	O	L	A
A	I	N	O	P	P	I	R	N	A	L	N	L	H
C	H	E	F	R	C	O	U	L	Y	S	S	E	S
H	I	L	H	I	L	H	E	L	I	B	A	N	C
I	N	A	G	A	M	E	M	N	O	N	G	O	A
L	E	U	R	M	E	C	B	I	A	C	R	R	L
L	O	S	C	A	R	T	I	V	A	R	T	A	C
E	S	P	R	O	N	O	H	A	R	T	I	U	H
S	H	A	U	P	A	R	I	S	E	Y	O	C	A
Y	W	M	B	R	O	C	K	B	A	R	N	E	S

In the word-finding grid, horizontally and vertically, there are 10 names of Greeks and Trojans in the Trojan War. Can you find them?

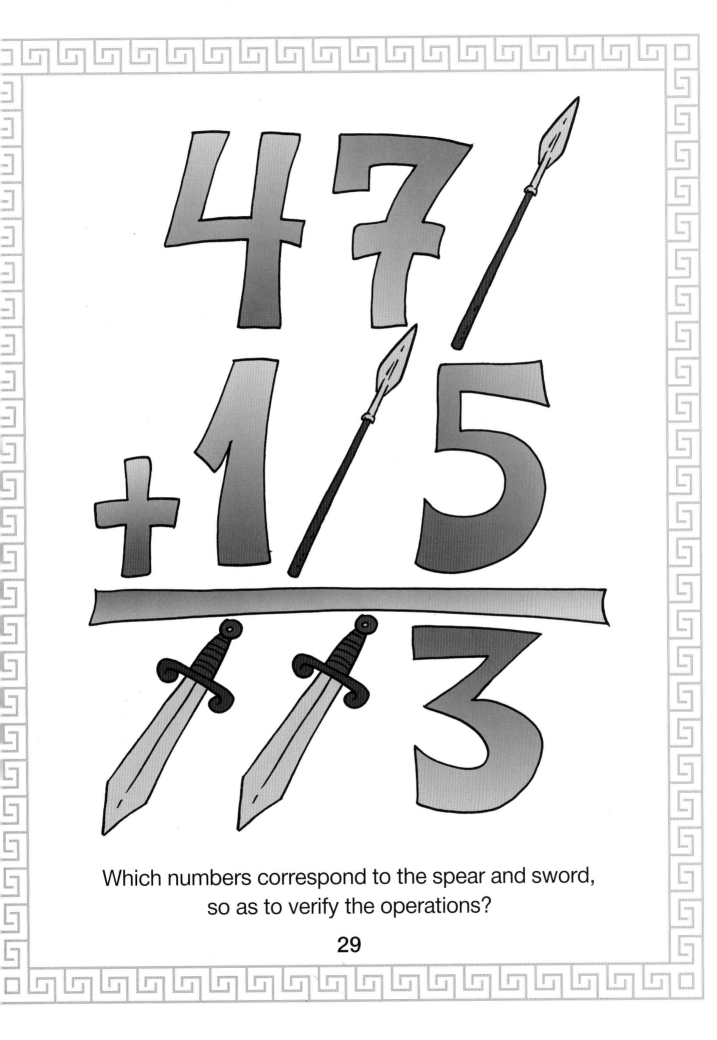

Which numbers correspond to the spear and sword,
so as to verify the operations?

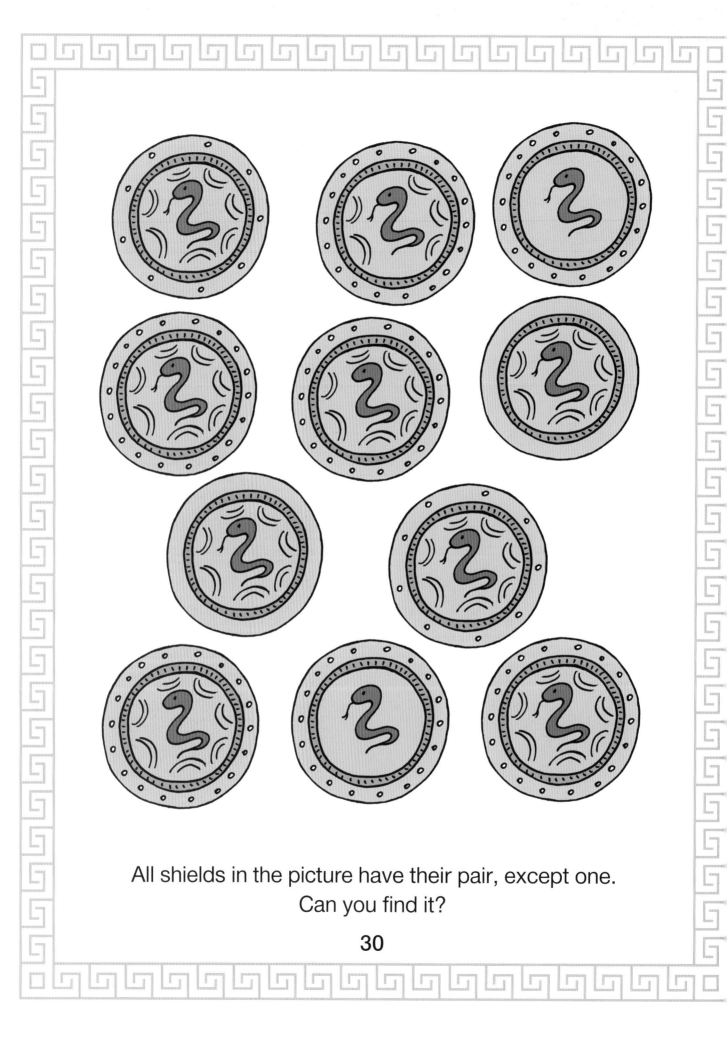

All shields in the picture have their pair, except one.
Can you find it?

30

Connect the dots from 1 to 72
to see what is sketched.

SOLUTIONS

PAGE 17 Path B.

PAGE 23 Details No 4 and 5.

PAGE 27 Shadow No 3.

PAGE 18

PAGE 24 Agamemnon wishes for CLYTEMNESTRA

PAGE 25

PAGE 28

PAGE 19

PAGE 29 Spear = 8, Sword = 6.

PAGE 21 Shadow No 5.

PAGE 26

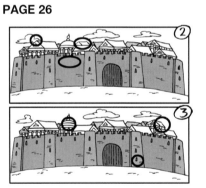

PAGE 30

PAGE 22

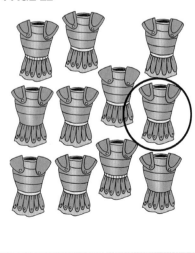